O COME, LET

G. F. HANDEL.

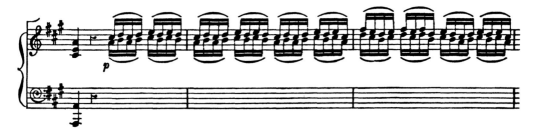

HANDEL

O come, let us sing unto the Lord

EIGHTH CHANDOS ANTHEM

for tenor solo, SATB & orchestra

piano arrangement from the score with additional accompaniments by Battison Haynes

Order No: NOV 070140

NOVELLO PUBLISHING LIMITED

-tion, let us heart-i-ly re-joice, let us heart-i-ly re-joice, let us heart-i-ly re-

-tion, let us heart-i-ly re-joice, let us heart-i-ly re-joice, let us heart-i-ly re-

-tion, let us heart-i-ly re-joice, let us heart-i-ly re-joice, let us heart-i-ly re-

-tion, let us heart-i-ly re-joice, let us heart-i-ly re-joice, let us heart-i-ly re-

-joice in the strength of our sal-va-tion, of our sal-va-tion, O

-joice in the strength of our sal-va-tion, of our sal-va-tion, let us

-joice in the strength of our sal-va - - - - - tion, let us

-joice in the strength of our sal-va-tion, of our sal-va-tion,

come, let us sing un-to the Lord,

heart-i-ly re-joice, let us heart-i-ly re-joice .. in the strength, in . . .

heart-i-ly re-joice, let us heart-i-ly re-joice in .. the strength of ..

let us heart-i-ly re-joice .. in the strength, in the strength of

15

come, ... let us wor - ship, and fall down, and kneel, and

kneel, and kneel be - fore the Lord .. our Ma - ker.

and kneel before the Lord . . .our Ma - ker. For

He is the Lord our .. God, and .. we are the peo - ple of His pas - ture, and the

sheep, ... and the sheep .... of .. His hand. O come, let us

wor-ship, O come, let us wor-ship, and fall down, and kneel, and kneel,

and kneel be - fore the Lord . . our Ma - ker, and kneel,

and kneel, and kneel be - fore the .. Lord . . . . .

. . . . .our Ma - ker.

SOPRANO.
Allegro moderato.
Glo - ry and wor - ship are be - fore Him, pow - er and
ALTO.
Glo - ry and wor - ship are be - fore Him, pow - er and
TENOR.
Glo - ry and wor - ship are be - fore Him, pow - er and
BASS.
Glo - ry and wor - ship are be - fore Him, pow - er and
Allegro moderato.
hon-our are in His sanc - - tu - a - ry, pow- er, hon-our,
hon-our are in His sanc-tu - a - ry, pow- er, hon-our, glo - ry,
hon-our are in His sanc-tu - a - ry, glo- ry, wor-ship, hon-our, glo - ry,
hon-our are in His sanc - - - - - - - tu - a - ry, glo - ry,
glo- ry, wor-ship are in His sanc - - - - - - -
wor-ship, pow- er, hon-our are in His sanc - tu - a - ry, are
glo -ry, wor-ship, hon-our are in His sanc - tu - a - ry, are
wor-ship, pow-er, hon-our are in His sanc - - - - -

hon - our are in His sanc - - tu - ary, are in His sanc

hon - our are in His sanc - - tu - ary, are in His sanc -

hon - our are in His sanc - - tu - ary, are in His sanc -

hon - our are in His sanc - - tu - ary, are in His sanc -

- tu - ary.

- tu - ary.

- tu - ary.

- tu - ary.

Tell it, tell it out a-mong the hea - then, that the Lord is

King, tell it, tell it, tell it, tell it out a-mong the hea- then,

tell it out a-mong the hea - - - - - - - - -

- then, that the Lord is King.

world so fast . . . it can - - - not be mov -

tell it,

world . . . so fast . . . . . it can - not .

can't be mov - - - - - - ed, .

- - - - ed, and that He made the

tell it, tell it out a-mong the hea - then, that He made the

be mov - - - - - - - - ed, and that He made the

it can - not be mov - - ed, and that He made the

world so fast it can - not be mov - - - - - -

world so fast . . it can - not be mov - - -

world so fast it can - not be mov - - - -

world so fast it can't be mov -

- - - ed, it can-not be mov - ed.

- - - ed, it can-not be mov - ed.

- - - ed, it can-not be mov - ed.

- - - ed, it can-not be mov - ed.

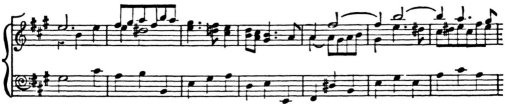

O mag - ni - fy the Lord, O mag - ni - fy .. the

Lord,   O mag-ni - fy . . . . the Lord,

O mag-ni - fy . . . the Lord, O mag - ni - fy the Lord,

O mag-ni fy . . . . the Lord, O

mag-ni-fy the Lord, and wor - ship Him, and wor - ship Him up-

-on His ho - - - ly hill, up-on His ho-ly hill, up-on His ho-ly

hill, and wor - ship Him up - on His ho-ly hill,

for the Lord our God is . .

ho - ly, for the

Lord our God is.. ho-ly, is ho - - - ly. the

Lord our God is ho - - ly, is ho - ly, the Lord our God is

ho - ly, is ho - ly. O mag-ni -

-fy, ... O mag - ni - fy.. the Lord,

O mag ni - fy, ... O mag - ni - fy the Lord, and

wor - ship Him, and wor - ship Him up - on His ho - - ly

hill, up - on His ho - ly hill, and wor - - - - - ship Him up

- on His ho - ly hill.

Andante con moto.

TENOR.

The Lord pre - serv-eth, the

Lord . . . . pre - serv-eth the souls, the souls of the saints, the

Lord pre-serv-eth, the Lord pre-serv-eth the souls, ... the souls, . .

. . . . the souls of the saints, . . .

He shall de liv - - er them from the hand of . .

. . the un-god - ly, He shall de-liv - er them, He shall de-liv - er them

from the hand of . . the un - god - - ly, He shall de

liv - - er them from the hand . . . . . .

. . . of th'un - god - - - - - - - ly,

He shall de - liv - er them,   He shall de - liv - er them   from the hand

of th'un-god - ly.

Adagio, ma non troppo.

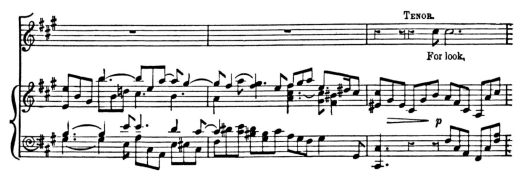

TENOR.

For look,

as high as the hea-ven is, in com-pa-ri-son of the earth, so

great is His mer-cy, so great is His mer-cy to - wards them . . that fear . .

. . . . . Him, so great is His mer-cy to-wards them that fear

Him, that fear . Him, for look, how

high the hea - ven is, in com-pa-ri-son of the earth, so great, so

great is His mer - cy to-wards them, to - wards them that fear . . . .

. . . . Him, to-wards them that fear . . . Him.

-joice in the Lord ye righteous,

- - - ness, joy - ful glad-ness, for such as are true heart - -

-joice in the Lord ye righteous,

- joice in the Lord ye righteous,

- - ed, and joy - ful glad - - -

- - - - ness, and joy - ful glad-ness, for such as are true

NOV070140

ISBN-13: 978-0-85360-385-6
Distributed By

HAL LEONARD

14023693

NOVELLO

Published by EXCLUSIVELY
Part of the Music Sales Group, 14-15 Ber DISTRIBUTED BY
Exclusive dist HAL LEONARD
Newmarket Road, Bury St

14023693
U.S. $11.95